Bond Assessment Papers

First papers in English

J M Bond and Sarah Lindsay

Key words

Some special words are used in this book. You will find them picked out in **bold** in the Papers. These words are explained here.

adjective	a word that describes somebody or something
alphabetical order	words arranged in the order found in the alphabet
antonym	a word with a meaning opposite to another word *hot – cold*
compound word	a word made up of two other words *football*
conjunction	a word used to link sentences, phrases and words *and, but*
consonant letters	all letters of the alphabet apart from a, e, i, o, u (vowel letters)
definition	meanings of words
dialogue word	the way people say things *shouted*
diminutive	a word implying smallness *booklet*
homonym	words that have the same spelling as another word, but a different meaning
noun	a word for somebody or something
collective noun	a word referring to a group *swarm*
past tense	something that has already happened
plural	more than one *cats*
prefix	a group of letters added to the beginning of a word *un, dis*
present tense	something happening now
pronoun	words often replacing nouns
personal pronoun	pronouns used when writing about ourselves or others *I, you, he*
possessive pronoun	pronouns used to tell us who owns something *his, mine*
root word	words to which prefixes or suffixes can be added to make other words *quickly*
singular	one *cat*
suffix	a group of letters added to the end of a word *ly, ful*
synonym	words with a very similar meaning to another word *quick – fast*
verb	a 'doing' or 'being' word
vowel letters	the letters a, e, i, o, u

Paper 1

All the summer through poor Thumbelina lived alone in the forest. She plaited herself a bed of green stalks and hung it up under a large dark leaf so that no rain might fall on her. She gathered honey from flowers and every morning drank the dew which lay on the leaves. In this way she spent the summer and autumn, but then winter came – the long cold winter. The birds which had sung so sweetly for her flew away on their long journeys. The trees and flowers withered, the large dark leaf which she had lived under shrivelled up and became nothing but a yellow, withered stem, and she felt frightfully cold, for her clothes were now all torn and she herself was so tiny and frail.

From *Thumbelina* by Hans Christian Andersen

Underline the right answers.

1 Thumbelina's bed was made of (wood, grass, <u>stalks</u>).

2 Thumbelina ate (bread, <u>honey</u>, grass).

3 In the winter the birds (slept, <u>flew away</u>, sang).

Answer these questions.

4 Why did Thumbelina hang her bed under a large dark leaf?

Incase it rains.

5 What did Thumbelina drink every morning?

The dew from leaves

6 Why do you think she was called 'Thumbelina'?

Because she's so tiny and frail

7 How do you think Thumbelina felt when winter arrived?

cold

8 What happened to the leaf Thumbelina lived under?

Shrivled up and became nothing but a yellow withered stem.

9 Which word in the passage also means 'shrivelled up'?

Withered

Add *ing* to the word at the beginning of each line and use it to finish the sentence.

10 help   I am _helping_ to wash up.

11 play   She was _playing_ with her toys.

12 fly   The plane was _flying_ overhead.

13 wear   Tara was _wearing_ her best dress.

14 kick   Tom was _kicking_ the ball.

15 read   The children were _reading_ their books.

Circle the **vowel letters** in these words.

16 te(n)n(i)s   **17** f(oo)tb(a)ll   **18** r(o)w(i)n g

Write out these sentences putting in the capital letters and full stops.

19–20 the holiday was great

The holiday was great.

21–22 the dog swam across the river

The dog swam across the river.

Put these words in the order you would find them in a dictionary.

cat   horse   pig   rat   dog

23 (1) _cat_   **24** (2) _dog_   **25** (3) _horse_

26 (4) _pig_   **27** (5) _rat_

Circle the **consonant letters** in these words.

28 (p)e(nc)i(l)   **29** (r)u(l)e(r)   **30** (r)u(bb)er

6

6

3

4

5

3

30
TOTAL

4

Paper 2

Kim and her mother were in a pet shop. Kim saw a black and white sheep-dog puppy.

"Look, Mum," she said. "He is lovely. Can we buy him? I promise to feed him, and take him for a walk every day."

"He is house-trained, and fond of children. He only costs £20," said the shopkeeper.

"No," said Kim's mother. "He is very nice, but I think he will be too big for our little flat."

Underline the right answers.

1 The puppy was (black, white, black and white, grey).

2–3 Kim promised to (feed him, brush him, take him for walks).

4 Kim lived in a (flat, house, bungalow).

Answer these questions.

5 How much did the puppy cost?

_____

6–8 Give three reasons why the shopkeeper thought they should buy the puppy.

_____

_____

9 How do you think Kim felt when she wasn't allowed to take the puppy home?

_____

10 Name one pet you think would be suitable for Kim to keep in her flat.

_____

6

Read the clues to help find the words ending in *le*.

11 You can blow it out.   ca_____

12 Do this to eggs and put it on toast.   scr_____

13 It is just above your foot.   a_____

14 Nearly a fall.   stu_____

4

Some of the words below should begin with a capital letter. Rewrite them correctly.

15–20 john and his dog smudge went to brighton for the day last sunday. the weather was warm although it was march.

_____   _____   _____

_____   _____   _____

6

Add a question mark (?) or full stop to each of these sentences.

21 I like beefburgers

22 Where is it

23 Open the door

24 May I have some

25 Is it raining

5

Write a word which means the opposite of each word.

26 big   _____   **27** old   _____

28 early   _____   **29** quick   _____

30 wet   _____

5

30
TOTAL

Paper 3

> 51 Low Road
> Tavistock
> Devon
> 17th October
>
> Dear Zoe,
> I am writing to tell you that my sister and I have a baby sister, and her name is Philippa. She was born last Sunday, and she came home today. She has fair hair and blue eyes. Jenny and I are very excited. I do hope you will be able to come and see her soon.
> Love,
> Charlotte

Underline the right answers.

1 Charlotte's sister was born on (Saturday, Sunday, Monday).

2 (Charlotte, Philippa, Zoe) has fair hair and blue eyes.

3 Charlotte has (0, 1, 2, 3) sisters.

⬜ 3

Answer these questions.

4–6 Which three people live at 51 Low Road?

_____

7 Why do you think Charlotte is 'excited' about her new baby sister?

_____

8 How do you think Charlotte would have felt if she had a new baby brother?

_____

⬜ 5

Put commas in the right places.

9–11 I like apples grapes plums peaches and pears.

12–13 Shall we play on the swing slide climbing frame and roundabout?

14–15 Jason collects ladybirds ants spiders and centipedes.

⬜ 7

Underline the two words in each line which have similar meanings.

16–17 large   small   big

18–19 hard   easy   simple

20–21 weep   shout   sob

6

Write the **singular** of each of these words.

22 cows _____   **23** roads _____

24 shoes _____   **25** bananas _____

26 footballs _____

5

Circle the **verb** in each sentence.

27 James plunged into the water.

28 Clare crept past the door.

29 Dan sprinted to the finish line.

30 Alice crawled into the kitchen.

4

30
TOTAL

Paper 4

If you fall over and cut yourself you should find a washbasin and wash the cut with hot water and cotton wool. Make sure that all the dirt comes out. Next, if you have some, put antiseptic cream on the cut. This will kill the germs. If you are going out to play again you should put a plaster over the cut to keep it clean. As soon as you can, take the plaster off, as that will help the cut to heal.

Underline the right answers.

1 What does the passage tell you about?
(What happens in a hospital, what to do if you cut yourself, going out to play)

2 Why should you put antiseptic cream on the cut?
(To make it sting, to kill the germs, to make the plaster stick)

2

Answer these questions.

3 Why should you wash a cut with hot water and cotton wool?

4 Why should you put a plaster over the cut if you go out to play?

5 What helps the cut to heal?

3

Imagine you were playing with a friend when suddenly someone came and pushed you over.

6 How would you feel if they had pushed you over on purpose?

7 How would you feel if they had pushed you over by accident?

2

Add the **prefix** *un* to the words in bold to make their **antonyms** (a word with an opposite meaning).

8 Shaun is not **happy**. He is _____ .

9 The wicked witch was not **kind**. She was _____ .

10 The spaceman was not **afraid**. He was _____ .

11 The teacher is not **fair**. She is _____ .

12 Those shelves are not **tidy**. They are _____ .

13 The fish have not been **cooked**. They are _____ .

6

Finish these sentences in your own words.

14 It was dark when _____

15 I wish I was still in bed but _____

16 I'm early because _____

17 Shout loudly and _____

4

With a line match each word with its **definition**.

18 midnight   feeling of fondness

19 diamond   middle of the night

20 starling   a common European bird

21 affection   a line of people

22 umbrella   a shelter from the rain

23 queue   a hard precious stone

6

Underline the **singular** nouns and circle the **plural** nouns.

24 bushes   25 monster   26 bus

27 churches   28 knives   29–30 fish

7

30
TOTAL

Paper 5

Now he was running up a hill. He was so tired he felt he could not go on, but he did. He couldn't feel his legs at all, and his chest felt as though it was on fire. His mouth was dry as he gasped for air. But worse than all these things was the terrible fear. Would it catch him? He didn't dare look behind him. Then he felt its claws on his shoulder. He had been caught!

Underline the right answers.

1 Who was chasing the boy?
   (another boy, his mother, a monster)

2 Did the boy get caught?
   (yes, no, don't know)

3 Where did the monster touch him?
   (on the legs, on the shoulder, on the face)

3

Answer these questions.

4–6 Write the words in the passage that help describe how his legs, chest and mouth were feeling.

_____

_____

7 What was the worst feeling for the boy?

_____

8 Why do you think 'his chest felt as though it was on fire'?

_____

11

9 Why do you think the boy 'didn't dare look behind him'?

_____

10 What do you think the boy felt as the monster caught him?

_____

7

Write out these sentences, putting capital letters in the right places.

11–13 ben and his friend went to london last thursday.

_____

14–18 they went to london zoo and oxford street.

_____

8

Complete the table.

19–23

	+er	+est
cold	colder	
tall		
fast		

5

Underline the **dialogue words** (the words used for the way people say things) in these sentences.

24 "Help, I'm stuck in the mud!" screamed Nasar.

25 "Where are you going?" Miss Thornton asked.

26 "Look at the clown!" giggled Caroline.

27 "I can't find my swimming costume," Joe complained.

4

Add another **verb** with a similar meaning to each group.

28 run, chase, _____

29 eat, gobble, _____

30 shout, scream, _____

3

12

30
TOTAL

Paper 6

Daddy fell into the Pond

Everyone grumbled. The sky was grey.
We had nothing to do and nothing to say.
We were nearing the end of a dismal day.
And there seemed to be nothing beyond,
THEN DADDY FELL INTO THE POND!
And everyone's face grew merry and bright,
And Timothy danced for sheer delight.
"Give me the camera, quick, oh quick!
He's crawling out of the duckweed!" Click!
Then the gardener suddenly slapped his knee,
And doubled up, shaking silently,
The ducks all quacked as if they were daft,
And it sounded as if the old drake laughed.
Oh, there wasn't a thing that didn't respond
WHEN DADDY FELL INTO THE POND!

by Alfred Noyes

Underline the right answers.

1 At first they were all (happy, busy, moaning).

2 They had nothing to do and nothing to (play, say, watch).

3 The weather was (wet, sunny, cloudy).

4 What did Timothy do when Daddy fell into the pond?
(laughed, danced, grumbled)

4

Answer these questions.

5 Who do you think took the picture of Daddy in the pond?

_____

6 Why do you think the gardener was shaking?

_____

7 Why do you think 'it sounded as if the old drake [male duck] laughed'?

____

8 How do you think Daddy felt?

____ 4

Two words on each line are **synonyms** (they are words with similar meanings). Underline them.

9–10	large	small	little
11–12	quick	slow	fast
13–14	sea	ocean	beach

6

Choose one of the **adjectives** to fill each space.

bright sharp scary rough rainy

15 ______________ light 16 ______________ pencil

17 ______________ day 18 ______________ film

19 ______________ sea

5

Rewrite the passage, putting in the missing punctuation and capital letters.

20–26 mum said that she would take paul to london to buy some roller skates they set off from walton at nine o'clock

____

____ 7

Use the pictures to help finish the **compound words**.

27 snow +  = ______________

28 sea +  = ______________

29 pine +  = ______________

30 foot +  = ______________ 4

30 TOTAL

Paper 7

A recipe

- Mix the Rice Krispies and sultanas together.

- Put the butter and golden syrup in a saucepan and gently heat.

- Add the chocolate and stir until melted.

- Then mix together the chocolate and syrup mixture with the dry ingredients until everything is well coated.

- Put the mix into paper cases and leave in the fridge to set.

Underline the right answer.

1 What is mixed together first?
   (Rice Krispies and syrup, syrup and sultanas, Rice Krispies and sultanas)

`1`

Answer these questions.

2–4 What three ingredients are heated in a saucepan?

_____

5 Why do you think it is important to mix all the ingredients so that everything 'is well coated'?

_____

6 Why will putting the mix in the fridge help it to set?

_____

7 Describe what you think this recipe is making.

`6`

_____

Write four more words ending in the *ly* **suffix**.

8–11 quickly _____ _____ _____ _____

Add the missing speech marks (" ") to these sentences.

12 Where are you going? called Mum.

13 Here we are, Tom shouted.

14 It is over there! yelled Sarah.

15 Shh, Tuhil is asleep, Dad whispered.

16 Quick, it is catching us! Gemma screamed.

Write the plural of each of these **nouns**.

17 gate _____ 18 track _____

19 bridge _____ 20 rabbit _____

21 tractor _____ 22 farm _____

Each of these words has two meanings. Write the numbers of the two meanings that match each word.

(1) a bird which swims

(2) a twig

(3) an arm movement

(4) to glue

(5) machinery used by the army

(6) to dip your head quickly

(7) movement of water

(8) a home for fish in the house

23–24 wave _____ _____   25–26 duck _____ _____

27–28 tank _____ _____   29–30 stick _____ _____

Paper 8

"Tell us a story!' said the March Hare.

"Yes, please do!" pleaded Alice.

"And be quick about it," added the Hatter, "or you'll be asleep again before it's done."

"Once upon a time there were three little sisters," the Dormouse began in a great hurry; "and their names were Elsie, Lacie, and Tillie; and they lived at the bottom of a well –"

"What did they live on?" said Alice, who always took a great interest in questions of eating and drinking.

"They lived on treacle," said the Dormouse, after thinking a minute or two.

"They couldn't have done that, you know," Alice gently remarked. "They'd have been ill."

"So they were," said the Dormouse; "*very* ill."

From *Alice's Adventures in Wonderland* by Lewis Carroll

Underline the right answers.

1 Who was telling a story?
   (Alice, the Hatter, the Dormouse)

2 What was the story about?
   (three sisters, three brothers, three friends)

3 Who was very ill?
   (Alice, the Hatter, the sisters)

3

Answer these questions.

4–5 Who asked the Dormouse to tell a story?

_____   _____

6 Why did the Hatter say "and be quick about it"?

_____

7 Why were the sisters 'very ill'?

_____

8 Do you think Alice, the Hatter and the March Hare were enjoying the story? Why?

_____

Fill each gap with a **verb**.

9 Matthew _____ to the football match.

10 Mum and Dad _____ the children on holiday.

11 Jess _____ some herbs in a pot.

12 _____ behind your ears, Tim!

13 We _____ the kittens at six o'clock.

14 The cat _____ the milk.

Match the beginning of each sentence with its ending. Write the number.

15 A book _____ (1) can fly.

16 A fish _____ (2) boils water.

17 A plane _____ (3) can swim.

18 A wardrobe _____ (4) has branches.

19 A kettle _____ (5) can be read.

20 A tree _____ (6) holds clothes.

Write these words in **alphabetical order**.

helicopter   ship   train   lorry

21 (1) _____   **22** (2) _____

23 (3) _____   **24** (4) _____

Circle the silent letter in each word.

25 knot   **26** wrap   **27** climb

28 wriggly   **29** comb   **30** knee

Paper 9

Chips

Out of the paper bag
Comes the hot breath of the chips
And I shall blow on them
To stop them burning my lips.

Before I leave the counter
The woman shakes
Raindrops of vinegar on them
And salty snowflakes.

Outside the frosty pavements
Are slippery as a slide
But the chips and I
Are warm inside.

by Stanley Cook

Underline the right answers.

1 There were (sweets, flakes, chips) in the bag.

2 The weather was (hot, wet, frosty, snowy).

3 The chips were in (newspaper, a paper bag, a carton).

3

Answer these questions.

4 What did the woman put on the chips?

_____

5 Why did the person blow on the chips?

_____

6 How do we know there was ice on the pavements?

_____

7–9 Find three words in the poem that describe types of weather.

_____ _____ _____

6

Underline all the words which should start with a capital letter.

10–14 cat   france   kite   joke

monday   henry   purple   cupboard

highchair   india   misha   goat

5

Write the **antonym** (opposite) for each word in bold.

15 Mum says I must stay **in**. I want to go _____ .

16 First I turned on the **hot** tap and then I turned on the _____ one.

17 Anne was **first**, but Sally was _____ .

18 I found the question **hard** but Tom found it _____ .

19 Goldilocks didn't sleep in the **big** bed, she slept in the _____ one.

5

Add the missing apostrophes (').

20 do not   = d o n t   **21** can not = c a n t

22 we have = w e v e   **23** we are   = w e r e

24 it is   = i t s   **25** did not = d i d n t

6

Circle the **adjective** or adjectives in these sentences.

26 The yellow butter melted.

27 Dad has smelly socks.

28–29 Natasha wore a long, pretty dress.

30 Henry ate the huge bar of chocolate.

5

30 TOTAL

Paper 10

There's an old green Fordson tractor in the back of Grandpa's barn, always covered in cornsacks. When I was little, I used to go in there, pull off the cornsacks, climb up and drive it all over the farm. I'd be gone all morning sometimes, but they always knew where to find me. I'd be ploughing or tilling or mowing, anything I wanted. It didn't matter to me that the engine didn't work, that one of the iron wheels was missing, that I couldn't even move the steering wheel.

Up there on my tractor, I was a farmer, like my Grandpa, and I could go all over the farm, wherever I wanted. When I'd finished, I always had to put the cornsacks back and cover it up. Grandpa said I had to, so that it didn't get dusty. That old tractor, he said, was very important, very special. I knew that already of course, but it wasn't until many years later that I discovered just how important, just how special it was.

From *Farm Boy* by Michael Morpurgo

Underline the right answers.

1 Where was the tractor kept?
   (outside, in the stable, in the barn, in the garage)

2 Did the tractor's engine work?
   (yes, no, sometimes)

3 Why did he have to cover the tractor with cornsacks?
   (to stop it getting wet, to stop it getting dirty, to stop it getting dusty)

| 3 |

Answer these questions.

4–6 What three things might the boy do while sitting on the tractor?

_____

7 What part of the tractor was missing?

_____

8 What job do you think the boy might want to do when he grows up?

| 5 |

_____

Write the **collective noun** to match each picture.

herd   flock   bunch   choir

9  _____

10 _____

11 _____

12 _____

Write the expressions in the table.

Hello.

Watch out!

Mind your head!

How are you?

Good to see you.

Take care.

13–18

Expression of greeting	Expression of warning

Add the missing exclamation marks (!) or question marks (?) where they are needed.

19 Be quiet_____

20 What is your name_____

21 Help_____

22 Hurry up_____

23 Do you want to watch a video_____

24 Is it big_____

Add the **prefixes** un or dis to each word.

25 _____even

26 _____obey

27 _____appear

28 _____tie

29 _____happy

30 _____agree

4

6

6

6

30
TOTAL

Paper 11

Sense of Touch

Touching

Touch is very important to us. It helps us collect information about things around us. When we touch something we know if it is hard like a stone, soft like cotton wool, rough like the bark of a tree or sharp like a pin.

Keeping us safe

We know through touch when things are hot and cold. If something is very hot, a message is sent to your brain to pull your hand away quickly so that you won't get burnt.

Blind people

Touch is very important to blind people because they can't see. They rely on touching things to find out what they are. Blind people read by running their fingers over a page and feeling little lumps that spell out the words.

Underline the right answers.

1 If something is very hot where is a message sent?
(to your head, to your brain, to your feet)

2 Why is touch so important to blind people?
(Because they like feeling things, because they like to read, because they can't see)

2

Answer these questions.

3 Why is touch important to everyone?

_____

4 'Sense of touch' is the main heading. How many sub-headings are there?

_____

5–6 Give an example of something that is smooth and something that is cold when you touch them.

smooth _____

cold _____

7–8 If you were blind, name two other senses you would rely on.

_____

Add the missing commas (,).

9–11 I'd like cheese tomatoes lettuce pickle and ham on my sandwich.

12–13 Dad went shopping to buy a loaf of bread some batteries a bar of soap and a screw driver.

14–15 At school we did maths played football painted a picture and read a book.

With a line match the **present** and **past tenses** of these verbs.

16 catch	made
17 make	drank
18 go	caught
19 run	went
20 drink	ran

Write all the small words you can find in the word *otherwise*.

21–26 _____   _____   _____

_____   _____   _____

Find the hidden words in questions 27–29 and then complete question 30.

27 chbusdf   _____

28 hlorrybnds   _____

29 nkgdjcoacht   _____

30 All the hidden words are types of _____.

Some questions will be answered in the children's own words. Answers to these questions are given in *italics*. Any answers that seem to be in line with these should be marked correct.

Paper 1

1 stalks
2 honey
3 flew away
4 *To protect herself from the rain*
5 *Dew from the leaves*
6 *She was very small, size of thumb*
7 *e.g. frightened, lonely, hungry, miserable*
8 *It shrivelled up, becoming a yellow withered stem*
9 withered
10 helping
11 playing
12 flying
13 wearing
14 kicking
15 reading
16 ten**n**is
17 foo**t**ball
18 r**o**wing
19–20
 The holiday was great.
21–22
 The dog swam across the river.
23 cat
24 dog
25 horse
26 pig
27 rat
28 **pen**cil
29 **rul**er
30 **rub**ber

Paper 2

1 black and white
2–3 feed him, take him for walks
4 flat
5 £20
6–8 *house-trained, fond of children, only costs £20*
9 *e.g. upset, disappointed, fed up, sad*
10 [*a caged pet or the like*]
11 candle
12 scramble
13 ankle
14 stumble
15–20
 John Smudge Brighton Sunday The March
21 I like beefburgers.
22 Where is it?
23 Open the door.
24 May I have some?
25 Is it raining?
26 *e.g. little*
27 *e.g. young/new*
28 *e.g. late*
29 *e.g. slow*
30 *e.g. dry*

Paper 3

1 Sunday
2 Philippa
3 2
4–6 *Charlotte, Philippa and Jenny*
7 *She has a new sister, likes helping with the baby*

8 [*feelings for or against having a baby brother*]
9–11
 I like apples, grapes, plums, peaches and pears.
12–13
 Shall we play on the swing, slide, climbing frame and roundabout?
14 Jason collects ladybirds, ants, spiders and centipedes.
16–17
 <u>large</u> small <u>big</u>
18–19
 hard <u>easy</u> <u>simple</u>
20–21
 <u>weep</u> shout <u>sob</u>
22 cow
23 road
24 shoe
25 banana
26 football
27 plunged
28 crept
29 sprinted
30 crawled

Paper 4

1 what to do if you cut yourself
2 to kill the germs
3 *To clean the wound, wash away the dirt*
4 *To keep the cut clean*
5 *Leaving the plaster off, letting air get to it*

6 e.g. upset, angry, hurt, frustrated, fed up
7 e.g. hurt, understanding
8 unhappy
9 unkind
10 unafraid
11 unfair
12 untidy
13 uncooked
14–17
[sentences finished in own words]
18 midnight – middle of the night
19 diamond – a hard precious stone
20 starling – a common European bird
21 affection – feeling of fondness
22 umbrella – a shelter from the rain
23 queue – a line of people
24 **bushes**
25 monster
26 bus
27 **churches**
28 **knives**
29–30
fish

Paper 5

1 a monster
2 yes
3 on the shoulder
4–6 He couldn't feel his legs, his chest felt as though it was on fire, his mouth felt dry
7 fear
8 He was out of breath
9 He was scared
10 e.g. frightened, terrified, fear, pain

11–13
Ben and his friend went to London last Thursday.
14–18
They went to London Zoo and Oxford Street.
19–23

	+er	+est
cold	colder	coldest
tall	taller	tallest
fast	faster	fastest

24 "Help, I'm stuck in the mud!" screamed Nasar.
25 "Where are you going?" Miss Thornton asked.
26 "Look at the clown!" giggled Caroline.
27 "I can't find my swimming costume," Joe complained.
28 e.g. dash, sprint, jog
29 e.g. munch, scoff, nibble
30 e.g. yell, shriek

Paper 6

1 moaning
2 say
3 cloudy
4 danced
5 The gardener or Timothy
6 He was laughing
7 The sound of ducks quacking can sound like laughter
8 e.g. upset, silly, wet, foolish
9–10
large small little
11–12
quick slow fast

13–14
sea ocean beach
15 bright
16 sharp
17 rainy
18 scary
19 rough
20–26
Mum said that she would take Paul to London to buy some roller skates. They set off from Walton at nine o'clock.
27 snowman
28 seaweed
29 pineapple
30 football

Paper 7

1 Rice Krispies and sultanas
2–4 Butter, golden syrup, chocolate
5 When a mouthful is taken you get a little bit of everything/all the flavours
6 It will set in the fridge because it is cooler than a room
7 A chocolate and sultana Rice Krispie cake
8–11
[four words ending with the **ly** suffix]
12 "Where are you going?" called Mum.
13 "Here we are," Tom shouted.
14 "It is over there!" yelled Sarah.
15 "Shh, Tuhil is asleep," Dad whispered.
16 "Quick, it is catching us!" Gemma screamed.
17 gates

18 tracks
19 bridges
20 rabbits
21 tractors
22 farms
23–24
   (3), (7)
25–26
   (1), (6)
27–28
   (5), (8)
29–30
   (2), (4)

Paper 8

1 the Dormouse
2 three sisters
3 the sisters
4–5 *The March Hare, Alice*
6 *He was worried the Dormouse would go to sleep before he had finished the story*
7 *They lived on treacle*
8 *[own opinion about whether Alice, the Hatter and the March Hare were enjoying the story and why]*
9 *e.g. went*
10 *e.g. took*
11 *e.g. planted*
12 *e.g. Wash*
13 *e.g. saw/fed*
14 *e.g. drank*
15 (5)
16 (3)
17 (1)
18 (6)
19 (2)
20 (4)
21 helicopter
22 lorry
23 ship
24 train

25 **k**not
26 **w**rap
27 clim**b**
28 **w**riggly
29 com**b**
30 **k**nee

Paper 9

1 chips
2 frosty
3 a paper bag
4 *Vinegar and salt*
5 *To stop them burning his/her lips because the chips were hot*
6 *They were as 'slippery as a slide'*
7–9 *e.g. raindrops, snowflakes, frosty, hot, warm*
10–14
   France, Monday, Henry, India, Misha
15 out
16 cold
17 last
18 easy
19 small
20 don't
21 can't
22 we've
23 we're
24 it's
25 didn't
26 yellow
27 smelly
28–29
   long, pretty
30 huge

Paper 10

1 in the barn
2 no

3 *to stop it getting dusty*
4–6 *ploughing, tilling, mowing*
7 *An iron wheel*
8 *To be a farmer*
9 flock
10 choir
11 herd
12 bunch
13–18

Expression of greeting	Expression of warning
Hello.	Watch out!
How are you?	Mind your head!
Good to see you.	Take care.

19 Be quiet!
20 What is your name?
21 Help!
22 Hurry up!
23 Do you want to watch a video?
24 Is it big?
25 uneven
26 disobey
27 disappear
28 untie
29 unhappy
30 disagree

Paper 11

1 to your brain
2 because they can't see
3 *It helps us collect information about things around us*
4 *Three*
5–6 *e.g. pebble, ice*
7–8 *two of the following – smell, taste, hearing*
9–11
   I'd like cheese, tomatoes, lettuce, pickle and ham on my sandwich.

12–13

    Dad went shopping to buy a loaf of bread, some batteries, a bar of soap and a screw driver.

14–15

    At school we did maths, played football, painted a picture and read a book.

16 catch – caught

17 make – made

18 go – went

19 run – ran

20 drink – drank

21–26

    other, wise, her, is, the, he

27 bus

28 lorry

29 coach

30 *vehicle*

Paper 12

1 slippers

2 what he bought the slippers for

3 no

4 *The dinosaur's paw was sore*

5 *roar*

6 [*answer stating what they think the dinosaur's teeth were for*]

7 [*answer stating what they would have done if they had met a dinosaur in a shoe-store*]

8 apples

9 churches

10 boxes

11 pianos

12 cakes

13 ducklings

14 "Come here!" called David.

15 "What time is it?" asked Bethan.

16 "Let's take Snowy for a walk," Nasar suggested.

17 "Please can I have a cake?" asked Rupa.

18 "Where are you going?" called Mr Davenport.

19 "Look at the swans," called Jess excitedly.

20 "What a lovely morning!" exclaimed Frank.

21 saddle

22 scarf

23 shell

24 splash

25 storm

26 He

27 They

28–29

    it her

30 They

Paper 13

1–2 a mother, a child

3 he had a pain

4 in the bathroom

5 *He wanted to read his new comics/rest*

6 *brown*

7 *He didn't want to have any brown medicine*

8 [*answer stating why they think the child didn't want to go to school*]

9 cutting

10 writing

11 running

12 riding

13 putting

14–19

    HAIR – short, curly
    SKIN – freckled, pale
    EYES – bright, kind

20 *e.g. clean*

21 *e.g. out*

22 *e.g. rest*

23 *e.g. bottom*

24 *e.g. difficult*

25 *e.g. young/new*

26 ?

27 ?

28 !

29 ?

30 !

Paper 14

1 coffee

2–3 sugar, bananas

4 beans

5 *sugar*

6 [*other things sugar is added to, e.g. cakes*]

7 *It is warmer in Spain and oranges need a warmer climate in which to grow*

8 goodness

9 helpless

10 useless

11 blindness

12 darkness

13 careless

14–15

    me, I

16–19

    you, her, we, them

20–21

    [*two sentences, each using different meaning of homonym 'tie'*]

22–23

    [*two sentences, each using different meaning of homonym 'calf'*]

24–30

    They had nearly made it to the shore. Suddenly there was a splash and Tom screamed. Hannah had

tripped and fallen back in
the water again.

Paper 15

1 The bear
2 The old man
3 tired
4 *So that the bear could
have the northland to
himself*
5 *He beat it out with his
great paws*
6 *Her breast burnt because
she was fanning the fire*
7 chuckling
8 [*answer describing how
the boy would have felt
when his father fell ill*]
9 **gh**ost
10 s**w**ord
11 **k**nee
12 bom**b**
13 **k**night
14 s**c**issors
15 Although tired and hungry,
Tuhil struggled on.
16 When you hear the bell**,**
go outside.
17 Hot and panting**,** Hannah
ran to catch the bus.
18 Monty sprinted down the
valley**,** jumping the
trickling stream.
19–22
salmon, spacecraft, deer,
sheep
23 *ladder – e.g.
equipment used for
climbing things*
24 *adult – e.g.
a grown-up person*
25 *saddle – e.g.
a seat used on a horse or
bike*

26 *canoe – e.g. a small light
boat*
27 France
28 Scotland
29 China
30 Brazil

Paper 16

1–2 on ledges of rocks, on the
seashore
3–4 beaks, feet
5 *Mud, moss, twigs, dry
leaves, grass*
6 *To hold eggs and nestlings*
7 *A young bird*
8 *A good, careful builder*
9 *e.g. She shouted loudly.*
10 *e.g. He feels cold.*
11 *e.g. He talks all the time.*
12 *e.g. She is in a hurry.*
13 *e.g. She is hungry.*
14 *e.g. He will swim quickly.*
15 ours
16 mine
17 yours
18 hers
19–20
sleepier, sleepiest
21–22
funnier, funniest
23–24
smellier, smelliest
25–26
messier, messiest
27 *e.g. shouted*
28 *e.g. screamed*
29 *e.g. moaned*
30 *e.g. called*

Paper 17

1 on a mountain
2 a stick
3 his father
4 *a golden monkey*
5 *Are you the old man with
the dragon?*
6 *The old man had never
seen the dragon*
7 He was bent and walked
slowly with a stick.
8 [*answer describing how
they thought Chin felt
when he got to the top of
the mountain and the
dragon wasn't there*]
9–15
wave, lift, jam, patient,
match, pen, fly
16 bunch
17 team
18 crowd
19 bundle
20 flock
21 swarm
22 *misbehave – e.g. to
behave badly*
23 *misspell – e.g. to spell
incorrectly*
24 *misfire – e.g. to fail to fire a
gun properly*
25 *misunderstand – e.g. to
not understand something*
26 but
27 and
28 but
29 and
30 but

Paper 18

1–4
It is a small black dog.
The dog's name is Mac.

The owner's home is in Moreton.

The owner has a telephone.

5 £10

6 *Phone the owner*

7–8 *e.g. upset, worried, concerned, frantic*

9 afternoon

10 buttercup

11 armpit

12 toothache

13–21

Proper nouns	Common nouns	Collective nouns
Birmingham	spider	swarm
Wednesday	chair	team
Matthew	seaweed	herd

22–23

Farm Animals

24–26

Dexter the Mad Dog

27 *e.g. Goodbye.*

28 *e.g. Watch out!*

29 *e.g. Excuse me.*

30 *e.g. Thank you.*

Paper 19

1 thousands

2 twigs

3 water

4 *Leaves from the trees*

5 *Tea*

6 *China*

7 *delicious*

8 [*answer stating whether and why they think this story is true or not*]

9 lantern

10 lemonade

11 lifeboat

12 lollipop

13 luggage

14–22

male	female	both
his	she	them
he	hers	ours
him	her	they

23 some, time, me, met, so

24 the, her, he, here

25 be, cause, us, use

26 with, in, it, thin, wit

27–30

The farmer stopped and looked at the goat in his garden, which was the fattest goat he'd ever seen. The goat had eaten the cabbages, carrots, runner beans, turnips and even the farmer's shirt off the washing line!

Paper 20

1 Chris

2 Chris's

3 tea

4 *Fancy dress*

5 *7th April*

6 [*answer stating party games they enjoy*]

7 [*answer stating surprise visitor they think might be going to the party, e.g. clown, magician*]

8 lovely

9 thankful

10 useful

11 honestly

12 careful

13 slowly

14–15

The men crossed the roads.

16–17

The children waited at the bus-stops.

18–19

The dogs sat under the trees.

20–21

The policemen ran to help the women.

22 First

23 Then

24 Afterwards

25 Finally

26 clean – dirty

27 correct – incorrect

28 honest – dishonest

29 there – here

30 difficult – easy

Paper 21

1 3

2 green

3 silver keys

4 Joan Aiken

5 *A spoonful*

6–8 faint, shrill, twittering

9 *They had wizened faces, stick-like arms and legs and were only waist height*

10–11

The **pretty** girl <u>ran</u> towards her friend.

12–13

Sid, the **miserable** lion, just <u>growled</u>.

14–15

David <u>tiptoed</u> down the **wooden** stairs.

16–17

The **old** man <u>chuckled</u> to himself.

18 remain

19 stretch

20 create

21 remove
22 are
23 am
24 is
25 am
26 I am
27 have not
28 was not
29 you have
30 would not

Paper 22

1 find a safe place to cross
2 when there is no traffic
3 keep looking and listening
4 *On the pavement near the kerb*
5 *Let it pass*
6 *To help teach people a safe way to cross a road*
7 *Yes*
8 [*answer stating the age at which they think the Green Cross Code should be taught and why*]

9–17

The wind rattled the windows but Judy wasn't scared. She snuggled up into her soft, warm, comfortable bed.
"Are you all right?" she called out to her brother.

18 yours
19 I
20 They
21 she
22 smoke – clouds of gas and small bits of solid material
23 reptile – a cold-blooded animal
24 nostril – the two openings at the end of your nose
25 unclear
26 fairly
27 goodness
28 thoughtful
29 disappear
30 mistrust

Paper 12

Dinosaur Stomp

I thought I saw
a dinosaur
buy a pair of slippers
in a big shoe-store
I asked him what
he bought them for
and he told me
his paw was sore
and what's more
began to roar
and showed me what
his teeth were for.

I ran like mad
across the floor
and bolted through
the shoe-store door
and nevermore
no nevermore
laughed out loud
at a dinosaur.

by David Harmer

Underline the right answers.

1 What was the dinosaur buying in the big shoe-store?
(slippers, shoes, boots)

2 What did the child ask the dinosaur?
(if he felt all right, what he bought the slippers for, what his teeth were
for)

3 After leaving the shop did the child ever laugh at a dinosaur again?
(yes, no, don't know)

3

Answer these questions.

4 Why did the dinosaur need a pair of slippers?

Beta The Dinosaur had sour feet.

5 Which word describes the sound the dinosaur made?

roara

6 The dinosaur showed the child 'what his teeth were for'. What do you
think his teeth were for?

The Dinosaurs teeth were sour Brotekling hum

25

7 What would you have done if you had met a dinosaur in a shoe-store?

I would ~~teak~~ run away to tear

4

Write the plural of each of these **nouns**.

8 apple *apples*

9 church *churchs*

10 box *boxs*

11 piano *pianos*

12 cake *cakes*

13 duckling *ducklings*

6

Add the missing speech marks (" ") before and after what has actually been said.

14 Come here! called David.

15 What time is it? asked Bethan.

16 Let's take Snowy for a walk, Nasar suggested.

17 Please can I have a cake? asked Rupa.

18 Where are you going? called Mr Davenport.

19 Look at the swans, called Jess excitedly.

20 What a lovely morning! exclaimed Frank.

7

Write these words in **alphabetical order**.

shell   scarf   storm   splash   saddle

21 (1) _____

22 (2) _____

23 (3) _____

24 (4) _____

25 (5) _____

5

Cross out the words in bold and write the correct **pronoun** above the words you have crossed out.

26 **James** was painting a picture.

27 **Annie and Tim** were playing in a puddle.

28–29 Watch out, **the stone** might hit **Jenny** on the head.

30 **The chickens** lay lots of eggs.

5

30
TOTAL

Paper 13

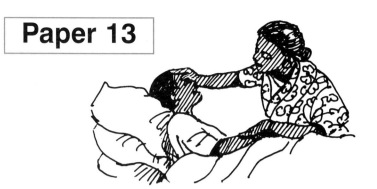

"Mum! Mum! I don't feel very well. I don't think I'd better go to school today."

"What's the matter? Have you got a pain?"

"Yes, in my tummy. It really hurts. I think I'd better just stay in bed and rest. I'll read my new comics."

"Well – all right. But first I'll give you some of that brown medicine. I'll fetch it from the bathroom."

"No! Mum, come back! It's all right, I mean I feel much better now. I'll get dressed and go to school."

Underline the right answers.

1–2 There are two people in this passage, who are they?
(a father, a mother, a teacher, a child, a granny)

3 Why did the child say he didn't want to go to school?
(he was tired, he didn't like his teacher, he had a pain, he had a cold)

4 Where was the medicine kept?
(on the table, in the bathroom, in the kitchen)

4

Answer these questions.

5 What did the child want to do in bed?

_____

6 What colour was the medicine?

_____

7 Why do you think the child got better so quickly?

_____

8 Why do you think the child didn't want to go to school?

_____

4

Add *ing* to the **verb** at the beginning of each line to finish the sentence. Don't forget any spelling changes.

9 **cut** Michael is _____ his birthday cake.

10 **write** David is _____ a letter to his friend.

11 **run** Caroline is _____ up the garden path.

12 **ride** Susan is _____ a donkey on the beach.

13 **put** Tony is _____ on his swimming trunks.

5

Put the **adjectives** in the correct columns.

bright   freckled   short   kind   pale   curly

14–19 HAIR   SKIN   EYES

_____   _____   _____

_____   _____   _____

6

Write the **antonym** of each word.

20 dirty _____   21 in   _____

22 work _____   23 top _____

24 easy _____   25 old _____

6

Add a question mark (?) or exclamation mark (!).

26 Where can I buy an ice-cream_____

27 Is it time yet_____

28 Hurry up or we will be late_____

29 Why do I have to wear this hat_____

30 Run_____

5

30
TOTAL

Paper 14

Food for thought

Have you ever thought how many different parts of the world supply us with food? Tea, as I expect you know, comes from India and Sri Lanka. The coffee we enjoy comes from Brazil in South America, and the sugar which some people like to put into tea and coffee probably comes from the West Indies. Chocolate is made from beans of the cacao tree which grows in parts of Africa. Oranges come from Spain, and bananas come from the West Indies.

Underline the right answers.

1 (Tea, coffee, chocolate) comes from South America.

2–3 What two things do the West Indies grow?
(apples, beet, sugar, bananas)

4 Chocolate is made from (leaves, stalks, beans).

4

Answer these questions.

5 What do we use to sweeten tea and coffee?

_____

6 What other things do we add sugar to?

_____

7 Why do you think oranges are grown in Spain and not Britain?

_____

3

Add the **suffix** *less* or *ness* to each word.

8 good_____ **9** help_____ **10** use_____

11 blind_____ **12** dark_____ **13** care_____

6

Circle the **personal pronouns** in the sentences.

14–15 Tell me a story before I go to sleep.

16–19 Did you tell her that we would visit them?

6

Write two sentences for each **homonym** (a word with the same spelling as another, but a different meaning). In each sentence the homonym must have a different meaning.

20–21   tie

_____

_____

22–23   calf

_____

_____

4

Rewrite the passage putting in the missing punctuation and capital letters.

24–30 they had nearly made it to the shore suddenly there was a splash and tom screamed hannah had tripped and fallen back in the water again

_____

_____

_____

_____

7

30
TOTAL

Paper 15

Long, long ago there was only one fire in the northland. An old man and his son took turns in caring for it, and kept it burning day and night. Their great enemy was the bear. He wanted them to die so that he could have the northland to himself. One day the old man became ill, and the boy had to look after the fire and care for his sick father. At last he became so tired that he fell fast asleep. The bear crept to the fire and beat it out with his great paws, and then went off chuckling. A little robin flew down. She found a tiny spark and she fanned it with her wings. After a while her breast was burned but she kept on fanning the fire till a fine blaze started. She had saved the northland! Ever since that day robins have had red breasts.

Underline the right answers.

1 (His son, The robin, The bear) was the old man's enemy.

2 (The old man, The son, The robin) became ill.

3 The boy fell asleep because he was (lazy, tired, ill).

3

Answer these questions.

4 Why did the bear want the old man and his son to die?

_____

5 How did the bear put the fire out?

_____

6 Why did the robin's breast turn red?

_____

7 Find a word in the passage that has a similar meaning to 'laughing'.

_____

8 How do you think the boy felt when his father became ill?

_____

5

Add the missing silent letters.

9 g__ost

10 s__ord

11 __nee

12 bom__

13 __night

14 s__issors

6

Add a comma (,) to each sentence to show where a short pause is needed.

15 Although tired and hungry Tuhil struggled on.

16 When you hear the bell go outside.

17 Hot and panting Hannah ran to catch the bus.

18 Monty sprinted down the valley jumping the trickling stream.

4

Circle the nouns whose **singular** and **plural forms** are the same.

19–22 horse   salmon   spacecraft

        deer   knife   sheep

4

Write a short **definition** for each word.

23 ladder _____

24 adult _____

25 saddle _____

26 canoe _____

4

Add the missing **vowel letters** to each word to make a country.

27 Fr__nc__

28 Sc__tl__nd

29 Ch__n__

30 Br__z__l

4

30 TOTAL

Paper 16

Nestbuilding

Birds build their nests in many kinds of places and use material such as mud, moss, twigs, dry leaves and grass. Some are skilful builders, while others make quite a rough and ready nest. A few birds make no nest at all, but lay their eggs on the seashore or on a ledge of rock. Birds use their beaks and feet as tools when they build.

Birds do not live in nests as we live in houses. The nests are made to hold eggs and nestlings, and in most cases are not used after the young birds have flown.

Underline the right answers.

1–2 Birds who do not make nests lay their eggs (on ledges of rocks, in bushes, on the seashore).

3–4 When building nests birds use their (hands, beaks, wings, feet).

4

Answer these questions.

5 What materials do birds use to build their nests?

_____

6 What are nests used for?

_____

7 What do you think a 'nestling' is?

_____

8 What do you think it means when the author describes a bird as a 'skilful builder'?

4

_____

Rewrite each sentence as if you are writing about someone else.

e.g.   I enjoy painting.   *She enjoys painting*.

9 I shouted loudly.   _____

10 I feel cold.   _____

11 I talk all the time.   _____

12 I am in a hurry.   _____

13 I am hungry.   _____

14 I will swim quickly.   _____

6

Underline the **possessive pronoun** in each sentence.

15 "That car isn't as good as ours."

16 "Sam's hair isn't as long as mine."

17 "Jack's bike goes faster than yours."

18 "That T-shirt is nicer than hers."

4

Add *er* and *est* to the words in bold. Remember a letter needs to change each time!

19–20 **sleepy**   _____   _____

21–22 **funny**   _____   _____

23–24 **smelly**   _____   _____

25–26 **messy**   _____   _____

8

Fill in the gaps with four different **dialogue words**.

27 "I promise I will be quick," Ahmed _____ .

28 "Run! David is catching you," _____ Clare.

29 Ben _____ , "I hate mashed potato."

30 "Please go and play for a minute," _____ Mum.

4

34

30
TOTAL

Paper 17

Chin has heard so many wonderful stories about the dragon who lives on the mountain that he longs to go and see it for himself. So one day he sets off along a winding path, all the way up to the mountain top . . .

At last Chin reached the top. There, in front of him, was an old, old man. He was bent and walked slowly with a stick. But if this was the man in his father's story, where was the dragon? The only creature in sight was a golden monkey.

"Hello," called Chin, "are you the old man with the dragon?"

The old man shook his head.

"What dragon? I've lived many, many years but I have never seen a dragon," the old man said.

From *Dragon Mountain* by Tim Vyner

Underline the right answers.

1   Where did the dragon in the stories live?
(in a valley, by a river, on a mountain)

2   What did the old man walk with?
(a monkey, a stick, a child)

3   Who told Chin the wonderful stories about the dragon?
(his mother, his brother, his father)

3

Answer these questions.

4   When Chin got to the top of the mountain what animal did he see?

_____

5   What did Chin ask the old man?

_____

6   Had the old man ever seen a dragon?

_____

7   Write the sentence in the passage that describes how the old man walks.

_____

8 How do you think Chin felt when he got to the top of the mountain and the dragon wasn't there?

_____

5

Circle the **homonyms**.

9–15 wave   hat   lift   jam   day

patient   match   rug   pen   fly

7

Underline the correct **collective noun** in the brackets.

16 Max gave Michelle a (bunch, forest) of flowers.

17 The (team, bunch) of rugby players got stuck in the traffic.

18 There was a huge (swarm, crowd) of people watching the clown.

19 We collected a (herd, bundle) of sticks for the fire.

20 The (flock, swarm) of sheep grazed on the hillside.

21 A (swarm, forest) of wasps landed on a branch.

6

When the **prefix** _mis_ is added to a verb it means 'wrong' or 'bad'.
Write a definition for each word.

e.g. miscount   _to count incorrectly_

22 misbehave   _____

23 misspell   _____

24 misfire   _____

25 misunderstand   _____

4

Underline the **conjunction** (a word that joins two sentences) in each sentence.

26 Swimming is good but netball is better.

27 I bought a T-shirt and wore it on Saturday.

28 Fred worked hard at his spellings but still found them difficult.

29 Close your eyes tightly and imagine you are flying.

30 I want a packed lunch but Mum likes me to have school dinners.

5

30
TOTAL

Lost!

Somewhere near Bramley Park
A small black dog called MAC
The finder will get a reward of £10

_____

Please phone the owner:
J. Brown, 17 Telegraph Rd
Moreton. Tel: Moreton 1234

1–4 Look at these sentences about this poster. Four of them are true but the others are not. Underline the true sentences.

The dog was lost on Telegraph Road.

It is a small black dog.

The owner's name is Bramley.

The dog's name is Mac.

The owner's home is in Moreton.

The dog has been found.

The owner has a telephone.

Answer these questions.

5 What reward will the finder get if Mac is returned?

_____

6 If you found Mac what does the poster ask you to do?

_____

4

7–8 Write two words describing how you would feel if you were Mac's owner.

_____ _____

Use a word from the box to finish each **compound word**.

| ache | cup | noon | pit |

9 after_____

10 butter_____

11 arm_____

12 tooth_____

Sort the **nouns** into the correct columns in the table below.

13–21   Birmingham   spider   chair   Wednesday

swarm   Matthew   team

herd   seaweed

Proper nouns	Common nouns	Collective nouns

Capital letters are used for all the important words in book titles.
Copy these book titles, adding the missing capital letters.

22–23 farm animals _____

24–26 dexter the mad dog _____

Write another way of saying . . .

27 See you soon.   _____

28 Beware!   _____

29 Pardon me.   _____

30 That is very kind of you.   _____

Paper 19

Thousands of years ago a Chinese Emperor was sitting by his camp fire, boiling some water in a cauldron. The fire was made from twigs broken off the flowering trees growing all around. As the water boiled, some leaves fell from the trees into the cauldron, and the mixture smelled so delicious that the Emperor decided to taste it. No one knows if this story is true but we do know that the Chinese people have been drinking tea for thousands of years.

Underline the right answers.

1 How many years ago did this story take place?
   (millions, thousands, hundreds, tens)

2 What was the Emperor burning on the fire?
   (coal, logs, twigs, paper)

3 What had the Emperor put in the cauldron?
   (milk, water, nothing)

3

Answer each question.

4 What fell into the cauldron as it was boiling?

_____

5 What drink had the Chinese Emperor made?

_____

6 After reading the passage, which country do we know tea leaves come from?

_____

7 Which word from the passage tells us that the Emperor liked the smell of the drink?

_____

8 Do you think this story is true? Give a reason for your answer.

_____

Write these words in **alphabetical order**.

lifeboat   lemonade   lantern   luggage   lollipop

9 (1) _____   **10** (2) _____

11 (3) _____   **12** (4) _____

13 (5) _____

Complete the table of **pronouns**.

his   she   hers   them   he   him   ours   they   her

14–22

male	female	both

What hidden words can be found in these words?

23 sometime   _____ _____ _____ _____ _____

24 there   _____ _____ _____ _____

25 because   _____ _____ _____ _____

26 within   _____ _____ _____ _____ _____

Add the missing commas.

27–30 The farmer stopped and looked at the goat in his garden which was the fattest goat he'd ever seen. The goat had eaten the cabbages carrots runner beans turnips and even the farmer's shirt off the washing line!

Paper 20

> 27 Kings Rd
> Welby
> Tuesday 3rd April
>
> Dear Jack,
> It is my birthday on Saturday and Mum and Dad
> say I may ask my friends to come to tea at 3 o'clock
> and stay until 8 o'clock. Please come in fancy dress.
> We will play games and after tea Mum says a
> surprise visitor is coming.
> I do hope you can come.
> Love from,
> Chris

Underline the right answers.

1 Who lives at 27 Kings Road?
  (Chris, Jack)

2 Whose birthday is it on Saturday?
  (Chris's, Jack's, Mum's)

3 What meal will they have at the party?
  (tea, lunch, supper)

3

Answer these questions.

4 What does Chris ask Jack to wear?

_____

5 What is the date of his birthday?

_____

6 What party games would you enjoy playing?

_____

7 What surprise visitor might be going to the party?

4

_____

Add the **suffix** *ful* or *ly* to each word.

    8 love_____
    9 thank_____
    10 use_____

    11 honest_____
    12 care_____
    13 slow_____

Rewrite these sentences, changing them from **singular** to **plural**.

14–15 The man crossed the road.

_____

16–17 The child waited at the bus-stop.

_____

18–19 The dog sat under the tree.

_____

20–21 The policeman ran to help the woman.

_____

Fill each gap with a word that shows the sequence of events.

    Then   Finally   First   Afterwards

22 _____ put toothpaste on your toothbrush.

23 _____ brush your teeth.

24 _____ you can rinse your mouth with water.

25 _____ get into bed.

Draw a line to match the **antonyms**.

    26 clean   dishonest

    27 correct   easy

    28 honest   dirty

    29 there   incorrect

    30 difficult   here

6

8

4

5

30
TOTAL

Paper 21

One evening Jem stepped outside for a quick breath of air, after giving his
mother her supper – milk and honey, which was all she would ever take, and
that no more than a spoonful – when he heard some faint, shrill, twittering
voices behind him, and turned round to see three strange little children. *Were*
they children? They had wizened little faces, and thin, stick-like little arms
and legs, and they came up no higher than his waist. They were all dressed
in green.

"What did you say?" Jem asked, looking at them in surprise, for he had
never seen anything like them before. Where in the world could they have
come from?

"If you please, master, we have come for the three silver keys."

From *The Shoemaker's Boy* by Joan Aiken

Underline the right answers.

1 How many strange little children were there?
(1, 2, 3, 4)

2 What colour were the children dressed in?
(red, brown, green, grey)

3 What had the children come for?
(milk and honey, silver keys, some new shoes)

Answer these questions.

4 Who wrote the book this passage came from?

_____

5 How much milk and honey did Jem's mother have?

_____

3

6–8 Which three words are used to describe the strange little children's voices?

_____   _____   _____

9 Why do you think Jem was unsure whether they were children?

_____

Underline the **verbs** and circle the **adjectives** in each sentence.

10–11 The pretty girl ran towards her friend.

12–13 Sid, the miserable lion, just growled.

14–15 David tiptoed down the wooden stairs.

16–17 The old man chuckled to himself.

8

Match the **synonyms**.

stretch   remain   create   remove

18 _____ = stay   **19** _____ = lengthen

20 _____ = make   **21** _____ = take away

Add the missing word to make the sentence make sense.

22 "We _____ waiting!" called the children.

23 "I _____ ready," replied Mum.

24 "Where _____ Billy?" she asked.

25 "I _____ coming!" he shouted.

Write the two words each word is made from.

26 I'm = _____ _____   **27** haven't = _____ _____

28 wasn't = _____ _____   **29** you've = _____ _____

30 wouldn't = _____ _____

Paper 22

The Green Cross Code

First find a safe place to cross, then stop.
Stand on the pavement near the kerb.
Look all around for traffic and listen.
If traffic is coming, let it pass. Look all around again.
When there is no traffic, walk straight across the road.
Keep looking and listening while you cross.

Underline the right answers.

1 First you should (close your eyes, find a safe place to cross, cross the road).

2 You can cross the road (when it is full of traffic, when you hear a noise, when there is no traffic).

3 While you are crossing the road you should (look straight ahead, keep looking and listening, shut your eyes).

`3`

Answer these questions.

4 Where should you stand when you want to cross a road?

_____

5 What should you do if traffic is coming?

_____

6 Why do we have the Green Cross Code?

_____

7 Do you need to use the Green Cross Code at night?

_____

8 At what age do you think we should teach children the Green Cross Code? Why?

_____

`5`

Copy the passage and add the missing punctuation.

9–17 The wind rattled the windows but Judy wasnt scared She snuggled up into her soft warm comfortable bed Are you all right she called out to her brother

_____

_____

_____

_____

Circle the **pronouns** in each sentence.

18 Is this cat yours?

19 I love cheese on toast.

20 They are always late.

21 Where has she gone?

With a line match each word with its **definition**.

22 smoke   a cold-blooded animal

23 reptile   clouds of gas and small bits of solid material

24 nostril   the two openings at the end of your nose

Underline the **prefix** or **suffix** in each word.

25 unclear   **26** fairly   **27** goodness

28 thoughtful   **29** disappear   **30** mistrust

9

4

3

6

30
TOTAL

First published in 1973 by:
Thomas Nelson and Sons Ltd

This edition in 2001 by:
Nelson Thornes Ltd
Delta Place
27 Bath Road
CHELTENHAM
GL53 7TH
United Kingdom

06 07 08 / 10 9 8

A catalogue record for this book is available from the British Library

ISBN 0-7487-6181-0

Illustrations by R. Barton and K. Kett
Page make up by Aetos Ltd., Bathampton

Printed and bound in Croatia by Zrinski

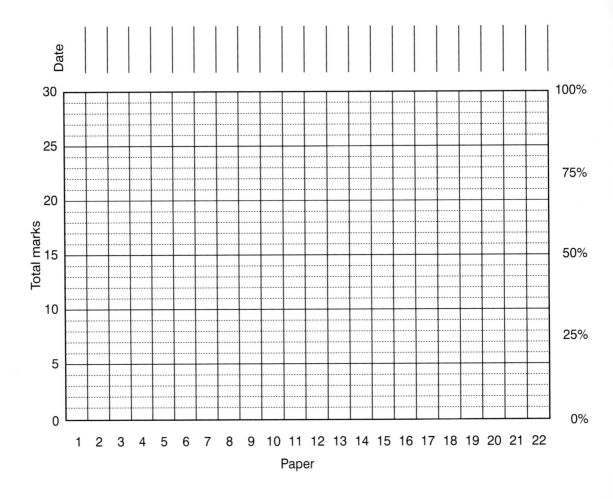

Date

Total marks

30 — 100%

25 — 75%

20

15 — 50%

10

5 — 25%

0 — 0%

1 2 3 4 5 6 7 8 9 10 11 12 13 14 15 16 17 18 19 20 21 22

Paper

Acknowledgements
The authors and publishers wish to thank the following for permission to use copyright material:
'Daddy fell into the Pond' by Alfred Noyes, reproduced by permission of the Society of Authors as the literary representative of the Estate of Alfred Noyes; extract from *Farm Boy* by Michael Morpurgo, reproduced by the kind permission of David Higham Associates; 'Dinosaur Stomp' by David Harmer; extract from *Dragon Mountain* by Tim Vyner, reproduced by permission of Harper Collins Publishers Ltd; extract from *The Shoemaker's Boy* by Joan Aiken, reproduced by permission of Hodder and Stoughton Ltd.